Trace Your Family Tree

Trace Your Family Tree

by Margaret Crush and

. . . . *(fill in your own name)*

Illustrated by Lynn Armstrong

This is a history of my family

My name is ....

I live at ....

I started it today .... *(date)*

.... *(signed)*

A DRAGON BOOK

Dragon
Grafton Books
A Division of the Collins Publishing Group
8 Grafton Street, London W1X 3LA

A Dragon Original
Published by Granada Publishing Limited in 1983

ISBN 0-583-30580-6

Printed and bound in Great Britain by
Collins, Glasgow

Set in Plantin

Contents

How to get started

Sometimes you may hear someone boast he or she comes from a very old family. So what? So do you! We all do – everyone is descended from the very few prehistoric people who were alive thousands of years ago. The only difference is that some people today know more about their family than others do!

But however much or little you know about your family now, you can easily discover some more. And you can start right now – today!

Ask your parents and grandparents, your aunties and uncles, to tell you about themselves and their families, what they did when they were little, what great events they remember, and so on. Get each one to help you fill in the page of this book that's specially for him or her. Ask too, if they have any old photos or souvenirs you can have. If a photo is a bit too big, you can often trim it without losing anything important in the middle, though do ask first if you can cut it. When you've collected information and photos, cut out the pages marked with a scissors symbol and file them in an attractive and long lasting ring binder. Extra photos (or ones that are too big, or too precious to trim) could be popped into one of those plastic envelopes that people use to keep knitting patterns or recipes in, and then filed as well. Set up a box for bulkier bits and pieces – your Family Treasure Chest (*page 67*).

Then you'll have a wonderful record of your family to show to other people, perhaps even to pass on to your own children. You'll never be able to find out everything though – no one does! Just think – if you could go back ten generations (a generation is about 30 years – the time between someone's birth and the birth of his or her parents), that's 300 years! With people having two parents, four grandparents, and eight great grandparents, you'd arrive at an amazing 1024 ancestors! It's very unlikely you would find out everything about all of them!

You can either do what many people do and follow back the male line of your family. This is because people usually take their father's surname, although some use their mother's maiden name (the one she was born with). Some people may have a new dad (stepfather) and have taken his surname, while others may have kept their original dad's name although their mum has taken their new dad's surname. People who are adopted can follow their adoptive parents' families.

Or, if you don't follow the male line, and know very little about that side of your family, you can trail other names. Try to find out the surnames of some of your four grandparents. Then follow one back – often the most unusual name is easiest, or you can find out many more facts about one name, which might specially intrigue you. If you do get stuck on one name, you can always try another.

Do write down *everything* you hear – even if you can't see any use for it at the moment. Genealogy (the study of family history) is rather like a jigsaw puzzle – the pieces gradually fit into place. It's rather like being a detective too – you are trying to unravel the history of your family. Sometimes the trail will peter out, other times it will just go on and on, and get more and more fascinating.

First things first – me!

But – first things first! Let's start with someone in the family you do know lots about – YOU. (*Stick a recent school photo of yourself here – or draw a self portrait!*)

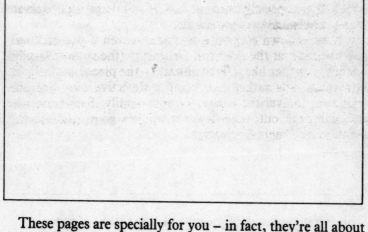

These pages are specially for you – in fact, they're all about you. So start your family history trail by filling in your own name and age and birthday on the next page. Find out, if you can, where you were born, and perhaps even the time of day. Find out from your parents, or another relative or family friend what nationality you are (British, American, Indian, Australian or whatever). Ask if you can have a photograph of yourself as a baby to stick in.

Turn to pages 11 and 12 – they're all about you too.

My full name is ....

I am ...... years old.

I was born on .... *(date of birth)*

Time of day ....

I was born at .... *(house or hospital)*

in .... *(street)*

.... *(town)*

.... *(county)*

My nationality is ....

(stick in)

This is a photograph of me when I was a baby/younger

I was ...... months/years old
(cross out the word which does not apply)

Me again!

I have .... colour hair.

My eyes are coloured ....

I am ...... metres ...... centimetres tall.

I weigh ...... kilograms.

I have/do not have brothers and sisters in my family (*Cross out whatever does not apply*).

I am the eldest/youngest/middle one. *Or* I come second/third or ...... in my family.

I have ...... brothers(s) (*fill in how many you have*).

His/their name(s) is/are

    .... He is ...... years old. His birthday is ....

    .... He is ...... years old. His birthday is ....

    .... He is ...... years old. His birthday is ....

I have ...... sister(s)

Her/their name(s) is/are

    .... She is ...... years old. Her birthday is ....

    .... She is ...... years old. Her birthday is ....

    .... She is ...... years old. Her birthday is ....

(*If you have more brothers and sisters than there are spaces for here, use this space for the rest*).

```
┌─────────────────────────────────────┐
│                                     │
│                                     │
│                                     │
│                                     │
│            (stick in)               │
│                                     │
│                                     │
│                                     │
│                                     │
└─────────────────────────────────────┘
```

This is a picture of me and my brothers and sisters/my house/a postcard of the town where I live (*cross out the ones you don't stick in.*)

I go to .... school.

My teacher is ....

Some/all of my brothers and sisters go/went to this school too.

I like these subjects ....

I don't like these subjects ....

My hobbies are ....

This is a picture of my pet/a picture about my hobby.

```
┌─────────────────────────────────────┐
│                                     │
│                                     │
│                                     │
│                                     │
│            (stick in)               │
│                                     │
│                                     │
│                                     │
│                                     │
└─────────────────────────────────────┘
```

One step back – my parents

Now you're filled in some facts about you and your brothers and sisters (*your* generation of your family), you have actually started in the very best place to make a family history. You have started with yourself – someone you do know something about!

Now you can start working backwards and find out more about other generations (your parents, and *their* parents – your grandparents), and with luck still farther back.

You are following the rules set out by all good genealogists (students of family history) – start from the person you know (in this case, yourself), and work backwards. Never take a person from the past who has your surname, assume he or she must be an ancestor, and try to work forwards to yourself. Even if your surname is Stephenson it dosen't mean that George, the developer of steam locomotives, is your umpteenth-times great grandfather. He might well be but, to prove it, you must first find out about generations much nearer to yourself – your parents and grandparents.

The next few pages help you to find out about your parents.

The best way to get the answers you want is to get your 'victim' – in this case your mother or father – to fill in as much of 'their' page of this book as they can. Try also to get them to chat about their lives before you were born, and you may discover all sorts of other fascinating information about their lives as children, what toys they played with, what they did at school, and so on. Jot down any extra information in a small notebook, so you can write it out neatly later. (There are more hints on 'interviewing' relatives on page 29). Ask too if your parents have any old photos, newspaper cuttings, special family 'bits and pieces' that you can look at and perhaps keep in your collection.

Everybody has lived through some great historical events – even you! Show your parents the Time Charts on pages 86–98 and see what great events they remember. They'll probably tell you all sorts of extra snippets of information about them. For example, just about everybody who is old enough remembers where they were in 1963 when they heard that President Kennedy had been assassinated. Ask your parents too for their autographs for page 119.

If you have a new mum or dad (step-parents) or you are adopted or fostered, and you know more about the people you live with now, then fill in about them instead.

By finding out about your parents, you're getting in practice for talking later on to other members of your family and finding out about them, too.

Remember with all 'family interviews' to ask your questions very politely – and remember too that some people are sensitive about telling their ages. So be tactful! If they really *don't* want to tell you, don't press it, but if you show them 'their' page of this book and fill in the bits they *are* willing to tell you, maybe they will overcome their reserve and get as keen as you.

So – let's take your family history back one step and find out a little more about your parents.

My mother

Her name ...Annie Mackay...

Her maiden name ...Macleod...

She was born on 17:6:1934... (*date of birth*)

at ...Cardhu... (*house or hospital*)

in .... (*street*)

...Scourie... (*town*)

.... (*county*)

Her nationality is Scottish. It is the same as/different from mine.

What she remembers best about her home/when she was a child

smell peat tilly lamps

writing to my brother.

What great events (like Coronations) does she remember?

War — remener german planes flyin over

fater Show me the stars.

What sort of clothes did she wear as a child?

Gymslip.

```
(stick in)
```

My mother when she was a baby/younger. She was ...... months/years old

(stick in)

This is a photo of my mother

What were her favourite toys – and what games did she like best?

black doll stone counti

bridman bussin moonligu

What school did my mother go to? *Scoure*

What subjects did she like best? *Spellin + Sums*

Did she learn any subjects I don't do today? What were they?

....

Has she an old school report or old school photo for my Family Treasure Chest? ....

What jobs did she do when she grew up?

....

Anything else especially interesting she told me

....

....

If you have a new mum (stepmother) and know more about her, then fill in about her instead. Or, if you are adopted and know more about your adoptive mum, fill in about her.

My father

His name ...William.. Robert.. Mackay

He was born on ...28.8.26............... (*date of birth*)

at ...Millburn............................ (*house or hospital*)

in .... (*street*

...........Skerray........................... (*town*)

.... (*county*)

His nationality is .... It is the same as/different from mine.

What he remembers best about his home/when he was a child

....

....

What sort of clothes did he wear as a child?

....

....

What great events does he remember?

....

....

(*stick in*)

My father when he was a baby/younger. He was ...... months/years old

17

```
(stick in)
```

This is a photo of my father

What were his favourite toys – and what games did he like best?

....

....

What school did he go to? ....

What subjects did he like best? ....

Did he learn any subjects I don't learn today? What were they?

....

Does he have an old school report or school photo I could have for my Family Treasure Chest? ....

What jobs did he do when he grew up?

....

Anything else especially interesting he told me

....

....

If you have a stepfather and know more about him, then fill in about him instead. Or, if you are adopted and know more about your adoptive dad, fill in about him.

If you can get a photo of your parents' wedding you could file it in a plastic envelope next to this page.

Two steps back – grannies & grandads

You have traced one generation back from you. Now go back another generation and talk to your parents' parents – your grandparents. This is where your real detective work begins.

You may get the basic information from your parents about your grandparents' names and perhaps their ages, but to fill out the picture and to get a strong lead to the next generation back (your great grandparents), you really have to ask your grandparents yourself, if you can.

Go and see them, or ring them up – or, if they're miles away, write to them. If you're going to see them, you should tell them in advance you're doing a project on your family's history. They may then dig out their old photograph albums and family papers before you come. Or, you can just take along this book and any other material you've collected, and get them interested by asking them to fill in their page.

Talk to other members of the family. It's not only your grandparents who may give you information – their brothers and sisters (your great aunts and great uncles) may also fill in the picture for you about their generation.

Your grandfather, for example, may even be dead, but his sister, your great aunt, may remember him well as a little boy, and tell you all about his model soldier collection, how naughty he was at school, and the medal he won in the war.

So, make a list of all the relatives you know (ask your parents to help you compile it). Then split it into two – people you see quite often or can arrange to see – and people you'll have to write to. (*See page 32 for a sample letter*).

Go and see the ones who live near you and chat to them. Note down everything they can tell you about themselves and what they know or remember about the family.

Grannies and elderly great aunts are often particularly helpful. Once they see how interested you are, they will often surprise you with the anecdotes and facts they dig out of their memories. Often, too, grannies and aunties are the ones who have the family papers, old letters, family bric-à-brac, the Family Bible if there is one, and so on.

If you are very lucky and your granny sees you are really interested and thinks you'll take good care of them (such things are very precious to many people), she may even give you her old photos. It might actually prompt her to do so if you show her your Family Album and Treasure Chest. Of course, you must never *ask* for them.

So, let's go two steps back – and find out about Granny's generation.

My mother's mother

(Genealogists call her my maternal grandmother)

Her name ...... Alexanderina Macleod

Her maiden name ...... Stuart

She was born on ...... 12.8. ...... *(date of birth)*

At ...... Elgin ...... *(place)*

What sort of clothes did she wear as a child?

long skirts.

What toys did she have? ......

What school did she go to? ......

Which subjects did she like best at school? Has she any certificates, photos or objects for my Treasure Chest?

......

Did she learn any subjects I don't learn today? What were they? ......

What games did she play? ......

What does she remember best about her own parents when she was a child? ......

......

(stick in)	(stick in)

My grandmother today **When she was younger**

What does she remember about the great events or wars she has lived through? ....

....

Did she go out to work when she grew up? What did she do?

....

When did she get married? .... (*date*)

Where? .... (*place*)

Where did she live after that? ....

Did she have other children besides my mother?

....

What were their names and birthdays? ....

....

....

Anything else specially interesting she told me

....

(*stick in*)

Photograph of my grandmother's wedding/the town/house where she lived when she was younger.

My mother's father

(He is called my maternal grandfather)

His name ...Alexander Macleod...

He was born on ....1897............ *(date of birth)*

At ....Polbain   Badcall.................... *(place)*

What sort of clothes did he wear as a child?

....

What toys did he have? ....

What school did he go to? ...SCOURE............

Which subjects did he like best at school? Has he any certificates, photos or other objects for my Treasure Chest?

....

Did he learn any subjects I don't learn today? What were they? ....

What games did he play? ....

What does he remember best about his own parents when he was a child? Mother died of measles when born brought up by granny. Fisherman/Crofters

(stick in)	*(stick in)*

My grandfather today   When he was younger

23

What jobs did he do when he grew up? ....

What does he remember about the great events or wars he has lived through? ....

....

Did he become a soldier/sailor/airman? ....

Was he a regular or did he do National Service? ....

Where was he stationed? ....

....

What does he remember best about it? ....

....

Anything else specially interesting he told me ....

torpedoed off Ireland
Survivers landed and invited
to a wedding that was
taking place.

(stick in)

Military photo of my grandfather/of the town/of the house where he lived when he was younger.

My father's mother

(Genealogists call her my paternal grandmother)

Her name .....Marrion Mackay.....

Her maiden name ...Mackay.....

She was born on .... *(date of birth)*

At .....Lotts, skerra..................... *(place)*

What sort of clothes did she wear as a child?

....

What toys did she have? ....

What school did she go to? ...Skerra.....

Which subjects did she like best at school? Has she any certificates, photos or objects for my Treasure Chest?

.....3 RSS...

Did she learn any subjects I don't learn today? What were they? ....

What games did she play? ....

What does she remember best about her own parents when she was a child? ...James.....Barbara.....Mac

.....Lott..

(stick in)	(stick in)

My grandmother today   When she was younger

What does she remember about the great events or wars she has lived through? ....

....

Did she go out to work when she grew up? What did she do?

Summ .Domestic Serv .... Herrueis Wick

When did she get married? .... (*date*)
Lerwick + England

Where? .... ~~See~~ Thurso. .... (*place*)

Where did she live after that? ...Millburn...................

Did she have other children besides my father?

....

What were their names and birthdays? ....

.... Neil .... 28.6.24 ....

Anything else specially interesting she told me

....

```
(stick in)
```

Photograph of my grandmother's wedding/the town/the house where she lived when she was younger.

My father's father
John.

(*He is called my paternal grandfather*)

His name ....James.. Mackay................

He was born on .... (*date of birth*)

At .....Milburn.................................... (*place*)

What sort of clothes did he wear as a child?

....

What toys did he have? ....

What school did he go to? ....Skerra.............

Which subjects did he like best at school? Has he any certificates, photos or objects for my Treasure Chest?

....

Did he learn any subjects I don't learn today? What were they? ......3 R's...

What games did he play? ....

What does he remember best about his own parents when he was a child? ....

....

(*stick in*)	(*stick in*)

My grandfather today   When he was younger

What does he remember about the great events or wars he has lived through? ....
....
What jobs did he do when he grew up? ..Shepheard/cow-..Fearn../..
Did he become a soldier/sailor/airman? .NO.............................
Was he a regular or did he do National Service? ....
Where was he stationed? ....
....
What does he remember best about it? ....
....
Anything else specially interesting he told me ....
....
....
....

(stick in)

Military photo of my grandfather/of the town/of the house where he lived when he was younger.

'Interviewing' tips

Apart from filling in this book, you could try 'interviewing' your relatives with a check list of questions (like the Super Seven below). Or perhaps you can jog their memories with an old photograph – or ask them to show you *their* photograph album.

The Super Seven essential facts you want to know are:

1 The full name of the person they are talking about and their relationship to them or you.
2 Dates (exact or approximate) of births, marriages and deaths.
3 Names and approximate ages of the person's children.
4 Occupations (people may have done several different kinds of job during their lives).
5 All the places where they lived, including addresses of any relatives who are still alive.
6 Any family 'papers' or photographs that might be useful.
7 Any traditions about the family's origins, e.g. 'I think your great grandfather came from Dorset – near Swanage, dear,' or any other anecdotes.

Tick off each point as you get the answer, though the information won't necessarily come in this order, especially as elderly relatives may ramble a bit. Dates and names may not always be right either, but they are something to go on – and you can always check them later against official records (*see page 111*). Also, if you talk to several relatives, you may be able to sort out some of these discrepancies.

You can sometimes get an approximate date or age by finding out how old the person was when a particular great event took place (*see the Time Charts, page 86–98*), for example, 'How old were you at the Coronation?' or 'Was your father born before or after the First World War?' However, as some people are sensitive about their ages, when you do find out something this way, don't shout it out triumphantly – just note it down quietly.

You probably won't get *all* the information at once either – especially as some elderly people have patchy memories. Try more questions after a time gap – they may have remembered some more.

Remember to give people time to answer. Don't jump in *too* quickly with your comments but encourage them to go on talking and telling you things by just nodding and smiling.

If you can use a portable cassette tape recorder *unobtrusively* and with permission, recording the conversation can be a help, though it may put some of your interviewees off!

You could try to persuade your older relatives to write their memories down for you. They'd probably enjoy doing it, and it would make a nice item for your Treasure Chest.

Always thank people for their time and help by giving them, later on, a copy of the family tree as far as you know it. (*Page 33 shows you how to draw one.*)

Writing to relatives

If the relatives live too far away – or you haven't ever met them, you *have* to write to them. You could, of course, ring them up (in cheap rate time), but it's best to write and warn them first. Then you won't take them by surprise, and they will have had time to think about what they can tell you.

In your letter, explain who you are, the names of your parents, and how old you are. Say you wondered if they could help you with a project you are doing on the history of your family. Tell them the name of the relative who suggested you contact them. Ask them, if *they* themselves can't help you, whether they could suggest someone else who can. There's a sample letter on the next page to give you an idea of the sort of thing to say. It's polite to enclose a stamped addressed envelope for a reply.

A good starter is to send them a copy of the family tree as far as you know it, and ask them to fill in or correct details.

Send them the Super Seven questions (*page 29*) and ask them to answer as many as possible about each person they tell you about.

If you get a helpful answer and your relatives are within visiting distance, perhaps you could then arrange to go and see them, or at least ring them up. Then you may find out a lot more general details and hear some interesting anecdotes. (*Follow the general tips for 'interviewing' on pages 29 and 30*).

25 Blenheim Road,
Woody Lane,
St. Albans,
Herts.

Dear Great Aunt Sophie,

My Aunt .... (name) suggested that I write to you. I am ..... years old, and the son/daughter of your nephew/niece.......

I am doing a project on the history of our family and wondered if you could help me.

I am enclosing a copy of the Family Tree as far as I know it. Do you think you could fill in any missing details you know about, or correct anything that's wrong?

I am also very keen to know more about Great Uncle George who, I believe, was killed in the Second World War, and my Great Grandmother Annie Stubbs who was in service in Dublin Castle about 1910.

Anything you can tell me about them would be very useful, especially their full names and dates of birth, and any other facts on the enclosed list of questions. If they have any other living relatives, I would love to know their addresses so I could write to them too.

I do hope this isn't too much trouble and that you can help me. If you can't, perhaps you might know someone else in the family who might be able to help.

I look forward to hearing from you. Perhaps one day I shall be able to meet you – I would very much like that.

Thank you very much for your help.
With best wishes from.......

How to draw a family tree

Now you've gone back three generations, it's time to put what you've discovered into a form everyone can understand. The best way to do this is to draw a family tree.

There are several kinds of family tree (*see also page 101*) but this is perhaps the best known. It looks rather like a real tree – with you as the 'trunk' at the bottom and the 'branches' of your ancestors spreading upwards and outwards.

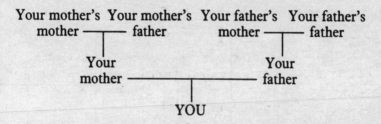

If you want to put in a bit more detail, say your brothers and sisters, or other relatives' brothers and sisters, you draw more lines sideways like this and put the eldest on the left and the youngest on the right.

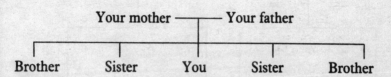

Now fill in your own family tree on pages 34 and 35. When you have cut the pages out stick them together down the centre with sticky tape and file them sideways.

My family tree so far

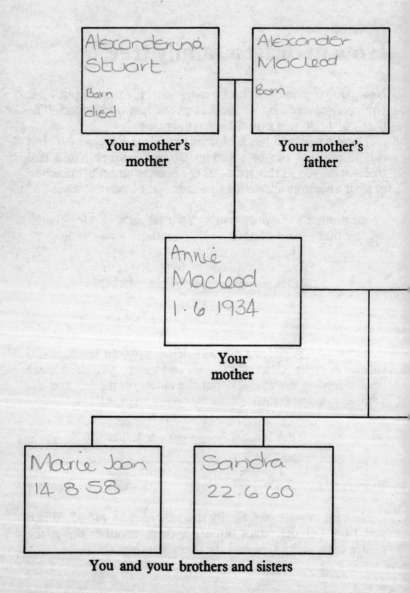

Alexanderina Stuart. Born died.	Alexander Macleod Born
Your mother's mother	**Your mother's father**

Annie Macleod 1·6·1934

Your mother

Marie Joan 14·8·58	Sandra 22·6·60

You and your brothers and sisters

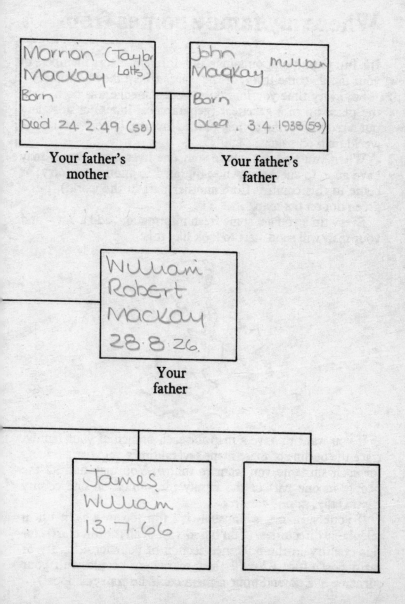

Morrion (Taylor Lotts)
Mackay
Born
Died 24.2.49 (58)

Your father's mother

John William
Mackay
Born
Died . 3.4.1938 (59)

Your father's father

William
Robert
Mackay
28.8.26.

Your father

James
William
13.7.66

Where my family comes from

It's fun to pinpoint on a map the different places members of your family come from, or the places where they now live.

So, every time you find out where someone was born, look the place up in a gazetteer (geographical index) or atlas and put a red dot on the correct part of the map opposite or on the world map on pages 38 and 39.

When you find out where someone lives now (people may have gone to another town, emigrated to another country, or come to this country from another part of the world), put a green dot on the map.

Every time you get some fresh information, add a dot – and your map will soon start to look like this:

If you want to have a map for each branch of your family, trace the outline of these maps several times, and use a tracing for each surname you want to follow. You may find all the people in one part of the family pinpointed on one county (Essex) say, or one country.

If your surname is unusual, it's fun too to look it up in telephone directories. (You'll find a set of all the directories for this country in the reference section of your local library or main post office.) You'll then see where people with your surname live now. (Some of them could be your relations!)

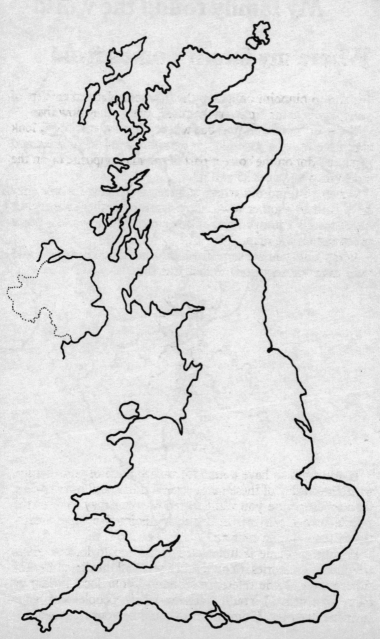

My family round the world

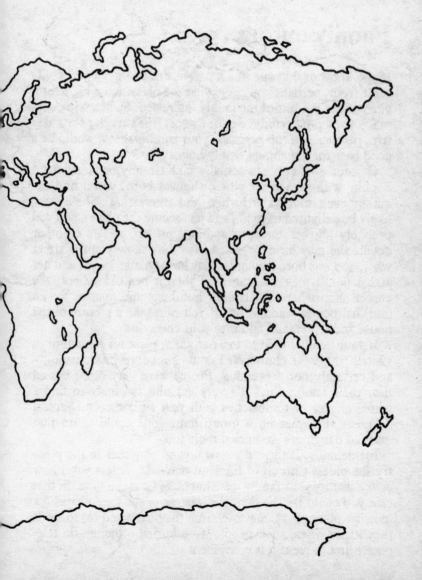

Family outing

If you know or find out which part of this country your family came from, perhaps you could visit the place. It's a big help if you can get the rest of the family interested. Such a trip could make a splendid family 'day out' – or, if it's too far for a day trip, perhaps you can persuade your parents that it would be a good base for the annual family holiday!

Of course, if you can actually take Granny or Great Aunt Sophie with you to see where she was born, you'll find the outing even more worthwhile and interesting. She'll very likely be delighted to come, and just seeing the place again will probably jog her memory and remind her of lots of other details she may have forgotten. She may show you the street where she was born (though it may have changed a lot, and her actual house may no longer be there); her old school; the corner shop where she bought humbugs and licorice for an (old) halfpenny – and so on. If you can, take a picture of the house and street, and add it to your collection.

If your family has lived in a particular place for some time, a visit to the local churchyard could prove very fascinating – and certainly not depressing. People were very often buried near their families and it's very exciting suddenly to find a whole cluster of tombstones with *your* surname on. Several different surnames on a group tombstone could mean that married daughters are buried there too.

Incidentally, if there are now several churches in the place try the oldest Church of England one first, unless you know *quite definitely* your family were not C. of E. at the time. In that case you could try the person in charge of the local chapel (or meeting place of whichever church they belonged to) to see if they know where such people were buried – though do telephone first to see if it is convenient.

Public cemeteries started in the nineteenth century so you could also look there, especially if you know your ancestors were not Church of England, as people of other denominations were often buried there.

These days some churchyards have been grassed over to make mowing easier, and old gravestones may be propped up against the churchyard wall. Sometimes stones are so overgrown with lichen that some lettering may be unreadable. Write down everything you are sure about, and often you can make a guess at missing details. Do always make it clear in your notes though that this is only a guess. Sometimes the local library may have copies of the inscriptions from churchyards which have now been landscaped or closed.

Of course, you must remember to treat churchyards and graves with great respect. Remember people are buried there, so it is a solemn place – not for running or shouting or doing any damage.

Look at the War Memorial – to see if any of your family died in the two Great Wars. Have a look, too, at the Church Electoral Roll (usually hanging in the Church porch). Does anyone of your surname still live there? Perhaps your parents might even ring them up and see if you could visit them.

Local telephone directories will also show you where other possible members of your family live in the district (though if your surname is fairly common, it's not always easy to decide if they are relations or not).

Side steps – aunts and uncles and cousins

So far you've been working backwards from yourself – through your parents to your grandparents. This is called by genealogists 'following the direct line'. So far, too, it's probably not been too difficult to get information, even though you may have some gaps.

Now – before you plunge any further back on the direct line to look at your grandparents' parents (your own great grandparents), it's probably easier for most of you to go *sideways* and fill in details of other people in your own generation – your cousins – and then their parents (your aunts and uncles who are, of course, the sisters and brothers of your own parents).

So – if you don't know already – ask your parents whether they had brothers and sisters. If so, what their names are, whom they married, and if they had any children. Then fill in pages 43–46 for both sides of your family.

Of course, you may know all this information already, because you see your aunts and uncles and cousins quite regularly, but these days many families get quite widely spread through work, travel and emigration, so you may very likely not know them. If some of your aunts and uncles live very far away, you might write them a nice letter like the one on page 32.

Your parents may have some photographs of themselves and their brothers and sisters when they were young. Or you might find a picture of your whole family group – cousins and all – perhaps at a wedding, or other family gathering. If you do find some, file them between the cut out pages 44 and 45 and after page 46, or, if they are too big for that, in your Scrapbook Album.

My mother's brothers and sisters

My mother has ...... brothers and ...... sisters/was an only child. Her brothers and sisters are my uncles and aunts.

Their names are:

			Born (*if you can find out*)
1	Jessie ②	Tommy ⑥	Year ....
2	John 1	John ④	Year ....
3	William ③		Year ....
4	Kate ⑤		Year ....
5	Lena ⑧		Year ....
6	Robert ⑦		Year ....
	Sandy ④	Buff ⑨	7.1.39

They married the following people (who are also called my aunts and uncles out of courtesy, though they are not related to me by blood).

Uncle ~~William~~ Sandy (*fill in name from above*) married Auntie Cathy

Their children are my (first) cousins.

	(*fill in this if you can*)
Their names are Sandra	Born ....
Ian	Born ....
Anne / Cathlene	Born ....

Uncle Robert .... married Auntie Ray ....

Their children are Linda	Born ....
Stephen	Born ....
Michael	Born ....

Uncle William ..... married Auntie Cathy .....

Their children are	Born ....
....	Born ....
....	Born ....

Auntie ..Kate.... married Uncle ..John Angus.

(add his surname)

Their children are ..Donald.... Born ....

..........Alexander.... Born ....

.... Born ....

Auntie ..Buff.... married Uncle ....Ian....

Their children are ..James.... Born ....

..........Evelyn.... Born ....

..........Alexdaur.... Born ....

Auntie .... married Uncle ....

Their children are .... Born ....

.... Born ....

.... Born ....

(If you have more uncles and aunts than there are spaces for here, fill in their details on a separate sheet of paper and file it next to page 44.)

(stick in)

Here is/are photos of some/all of my aunts and uncles and cousins.

My father's brothers and sisters

My father had ..**1**.. brothers and ..—.. sisters/was an only child. His brothers and sisters are my uncles and aunts.

Their names are:

Born (*if you can find it out*)

1 ...**Neil**... Year ....
2 .... Year ....
3 .... Year ....
4 .... Year ....
5 .... Year ....
6 .... Year ....

They married the following people (who are also called my aunts and uncles out of courtesy, though they are not related to me by blood).

Uncle ..**Neil** (*fill in name from above*) married Auntie ....

Their children are my (first) cousins.

(*fill in this if you can*)

Their names are .... Born ....
.... Born ....
.... Born ....

Uncle .... married Auntie ....
Their children are .... Born ....
.... Born ....
.... Born ....

Uncle .... married Auntie ....
Their children are .... Born ....
.... Born ....
.... Born ....

Auntie .... married Uncle ....

(add his surname)

Their children are .... Born ....

.... Born ....

.... Born ....

Auntie .... married Uncle ....

Their children are .... Born ....

.... Born ....

.... Born ....

Auntie .... married Uncle ....

Their children are .... Born ....

.... Born ....

.... Born ....

(If you have more uncles and aunts than there are spaces for here, fill in their details on a separate sheet of paper and file it next to page 46.)

(stick in)

Here is/are photos of some/all of my aunts and uncles and cousins.

Side steps back – great aunts and great uncles

Now you have filled out your own and your parents' generations, it's time to try to get more details about the next generation back – your grandparents' brothers and sisters. These are officially called your great uncles and great aunts – even though if you meet them you may often call them just 'Auntie' and 'Uncle' – like your real aunts and uncles (your parents' brothers and sisters).

Find out if your grandparents (on both your father's and your mother's side) had brothers and sisters, whom they married and if they had children. Then fill in as much as you can of pages 49–56, though don't be too depressed if you have to leave gaps.

You may find it quite difficult to find out the names of *all* your great aunts' and great uncles' children, though with luck your grannies *may* remember them. If it's all too difficult, don't get discouraged – most family historians have similar problems. Either leave the pages blank or partly blank, or write and stick in pictures of the great events you think your great aunts and great uncles may have lived through (perhaps the First or Second World Wars, the Great Depression, or the General Strike of 1926). Or stick in an old photo of your granny or grandad and their brothers and sisters when they were children and write underneath who they all were. Your granny should remember *these* names fairly well. Or think up some other way to use the pages, perhaps for sticking in extra pictures of your family or great events.

There are some splendidly complicated names for various kinds of cousins and knowing them is a great way of airing your knowledge, and settling family arguments – if it doesn't stir some more up! It all depends whether they are the children of your own aunts and uncles, or of your cousins, or of your parents' cousins.

The terms often get mixed up, or used loosely, but they are supposed to show whether relations are on the same *level* of descent from a common ancestor (a great grandfather perhaps) or on a different level (called 'removed'). How does it work?

Basically, the children of your aunts and uncles are your first cousins (because you are both on the same level of descent from your grandparents). Children of first cousins are second cousins to each other because again they are on the same level of descent, but to someone *not* on the same level they are first cousins once (or twice) removed. So your own first cousins' children will be second cousins to *your* children, but first cousins once removed to you! Your parents' cousins will also be *your* first cousins once removed, and *their* children will be your second cousins.

The children of second cousins are *third cousins* to each other, but to someone not on the same level of descent they are first (or second) cousins once, twice, three times removed!

However, to confuse you even further, the term 'second cousin' is sometimes loosely used for the child of a first cousin (strictly, as you now know, a first cousin once removed)!

So now you know – or do you?

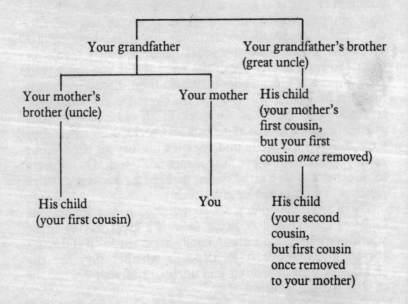

48

My mother's mother's brothers and sisters

My mother's mother is/was Granny .... (*first name*) .... (*maiden name*) She had ...... brothers and ...... sisters/was an only child. Her brothers and sisters are my great uncles and aunts.

Their names are:

	Born (*fill this in if you can*)
1	Born about ....
2	Born about ....
3	Born about ....
4	Born about ....
5	Born about ....
6	Born about ....

They married the following people (by courtesy called my Great Aunts and Great Uncles too, though they are not related by blood).

Great Uncle .... married Great Aunt ....

Their children are ....

....

....

They are my first cousins once removed.

Great Uncle .... married Great Aunt ....

Their children are ....

....

....

Great Uncle .... married Great Aunt ....

Their children are ....

....

....

Great Aunt .... married Great Uncle ....
.... (*add his surname if you can find it out*)
Their children are ....
                      ....
                      ....

Great Aunt .... married Great Uncle ....
.... (*add his surname if you can find it out*)
Their children are ....
                      ....
                      ....

Great Aunt .... married Great Uncle ....
.... (*add his surname if you can find it out*)
Their children are ....
                      ....
                      ....

(*If you have more great uncles and aunts than there are spaces for here and on pages 51–56, fill in their details on separate sheets of paper and file them next to these pages.*)

(*stick in*)

Photo of my grandmother with her brothers and sisters/or another photo or souvenir of her family.

My mother's father's brothers and sisters

My mother's father is/was Grandfather .... *Alexander* (*first name*) .... (*surname*) He had ...... brothers and ...... sisters/was an only child. His brothers and sisters are my great uncles and aunts.

Their names are:

Born (*fill this in if you can*)

1 ...... *Annie* ...... Born about ....

2 .... Born about ....

3 .... Born about ....

4 .... Born about ....

5 .... Born about ....

6 .... Born about ....

They married the following people (by courtesy called my Great Aunts and Great Uncles too, though they are not related by blood).

Great Uncle .... married Great Aunt ....

Their children are ....

....

....

They are my first cousins once removed.

Great Uncle .... married Great Aunt ....

Their children are ....

....

....

Great Uncle .... married Great Aunt ....

Their children are ....

....

....

51

Great Aunt ...Annie... married Great Uncle ...Bill Sutheh...

.... (*add his surname if you can find it out*)

Their children are ...Herbie..... ...Alfie...........

...Davy......... ....

...Walter...... ....

Great Aunt .... married Great Uncle ....

.... (*add his surname if you can find it out*)

Their children are ....

....

....

Great Aunt .... married Great Uncle ....

.... (*add his surname if you can find it out*)

Their children are ....

....

....

(*stick in*)

Photo of my grandfather with his brothers and sisters/or another photo or souvenir of his family.

My father's mother's brothers and sisters

My father's mother is/was Granny .... (*first name*) .... (*maiden name*) She had ...... brothers and ...... sisters/was an only child. Her brothers and sisters are my great uncles and aunts.

Their names are:

Born (*fill this in if you can*)

1 ...Ina................................. Born about ....
2 ...Kitty - Catherin............ Born about ....
3 ...Etta....Henry............... Born about ....
4 ...William........................ Born about ....
5 ...Marra.......................... Born about ....
6 ...Donald........................ Born about ....

They married the following people (by courtesy called my Great Aunts and Great Uncles too, though they are not related by blood).

Great Uncle .... married Great Aunt ....

Their children are ....

....

....

They are my first cousins once removed.

Great Uncle .... married Great Aunt ....

Their children are ....

....

....

Great Uncle .... married Great Aunt ....

Their children are ....

....

....

53

Great Aunt ...Ina...... married Great Uncle ...Jimmy...
...Miller............... (*add his surname if you can find it out*)
Their children are .Barbara.   ....
....
....

Great Aunt ..Kitty.. married Great Uncle ....
...Arthur............... (*add his surname if you can find it out*)
Their children are .Catherine   ....
........................Angela....   ....
....

Great Aunt .... married Great Uncle ....
.... (*add his surname if you can find it out*)
Their children are ....
....
....

(*stick in*)

Photo of my grandmother with her brothers and sisters/or another photo or souvenir of her family.

My father's father's brothers and sisters

My father's father is/was Grandfather .....John...... (*first name*) .... (*surname*) He had ...... brothers and ...... sisters/was an only child. His brothers and sisters are my great uncles and aunts.

Great GrandFath
Neil

Their names are:

Born (*fill this in if you can*)

1 ...Robert.. Born about ....
2 ...William Angus..................... Born about ....
3 ...Jean.. Born about ....
4 ...Johanne................................ Born about ....
5 ...Bella.. Born about ....
6 .... Born about ....

They married the following people (by courtesy called my Great Aunts and Great Uncles too, though they are not related by blood).

Great Uncle .... married Great Aunt ....

Their children are ....

....

....

They are my first cousins once removed.

Great Uncle .... married Great Aunt ....

Their children are ....

....

....

Great Uncle .... married Great Aunt ....

Their children are ....

....

....

Great Aunt .... married Great Uncle ....
.... (*add his surname if you can find it out*)
Their children are ....
....
....

Great Aunt .... married Great Uncle ....
.... (*add his surname if you can find it out*)
Their children are ....
....
....

Great Aunt .... married Great Uncle ....
.... (*add his surname if you can find it out*)
Their children are ....
....
....

(*stick in*)

Photo of my grandfather with his brothers and sisters/or another photo or souvenir of his family.

Three steps back – my great grandparents

Now we've gone sideways, let's get back to the direct line and your great grandparents (your grandparents' parents). Like everyone, you will have had eight great-grandparents, even if you don't know who all of them were, or can't find out much about them. Your mother will have had two grannies and two grandpas – as you have – and so will your father. Try asking their children (your own grandparents or your great aunts and great uncles) and you may be able to fill in some, if not all, of the details on pages 59–62. However, you may find it quite difficult to find out very much, if anything, about all eight of them – so don't be too depressed if you can't.

In fact, though you may not think it, you are actually quite lucky to be doing your family history *now*. Some, if not all, of your grandparents, great aunts and great uncles are probably still alive and able to be questioned about *their* parents. In fact, you may even have a great grandparent still alive! People who start family research later on in life will probably not be so lucky, as many, if not all, of their grandparents' generation will usually have died.

You can, of course, pursue your great grandparents through the official records (*see page 111*). If you find out, say, the date of birth of your eldest great aunt or great uncle, try to look at the birth certificate at St Catherine's House. That will get you the names of both of his or her parents (your great grandparents) and probably the father's occupation. You may be able to trace those parents' marriage and this will show *where* they were living then, and possibly their ages – which will give you their dates of birth – and so on. The census records (*see page 114*) might help.

However, your detective work does get very complicated now – so it's best to get as much oral (spoken) information as you can before you plunge into official records.

If you do manage to find out a fair bit about your great grandparents (or at least some of them) and want to delve further back, you do have *eight* names to choose from. You can either follow just one line, say your mother's family, taking her maiden name as a start, or your father's side. This book puts the female (mother's) line first, but most genealogists would follow the male line because that's usually where the surname is handed down.

So – great grandparents – here we come!

Great grandparents – my mother's side

This page is about the parents of my grandmother (my mother's mother).

My great grandfather's name was ....

He was born about .... (*year*) .... (*place*)

His job was ....

He died about .... (*year*)

He would have remembered/been alive during this great event

....

Anything else I know about him ....

....

My great grandmother's name was ....

Her maiden name was ....

She was born about .... (*year*) .... (*place*)

She had ...... children.

She died about .... (*year*)

She would have remembered/been alive during this great event. ....

Anything else I know about her ....

....

┌─────────────────────────────────┐
│   │
│   │
│   │
│   (*stick in*)   │
│   │
│   │
│   │
└─────────────────────────────────┘

This is a photo or souvenir of these great grandparents.

This page is about the parents of my grandfather (my mother's father).

My great grandfather's name was ....

He was born about .... (*year*) .... (*place*)

His job was ....

He died about .... (*year*)

He might have remembered/been alive during this great event

....

Anything else I know about him ....

....

My great grandmother's name was ....

Her maiden name was ....

She was born about .... (*year*) .... (*place*)

She had ...... children.

She died about .... (*year*)

She might have remembered/been alive during this great event. ....

Anything else I know about her ....

....

(*stick in*)

This is a photo or souvenir of these great grandparents.

Great grandparents – my father's side

This page is about the parents of my grandmother (my father's mother).

My great grandfather's name was ....

He was born about .... (*year*) .... (*place*)

His job was ....

He died about .... (*year*)

He would have remembered/been alive during this great event

....

Anything else I know about him ....

....

My great grandmother's name was ....

Her maiden name was ....

She was born about .... (*year*) .... (*place*)

She had ...... children.

She died about .... (*year*)

She would have remembered/been alive during this great event...

Anything else I know about her ....

....

┌─────────────────────────────────┐
│   │
│   │
│   │
│   (*stick in*)   │
│   │
│   │
└─────────────────────────────────┘

This is a photo or souvenir of these great grandparents.

This page is about the parents of my grandfather (my father's father).

My great grandfather's name was ....

He was born about .... (*year*) .... (*place*)

His job was ....

He died about .... (*year*)

He would have remembered/been alive during this great event

....

Anything else I know about him ....

....

My great grandmother's name was ....

Her maiden name was ....

She was born about .... (*year*) .... (*place*)

She had ...... children.

She died about .... (*year*)

She would have remembered/been alive during this great event. ....

Anything else I know about her ....

....

(*stick in*)

This is a photo or souvenir of these great grandparents.

My family tree is longer now!

So now you can fill in a longer family tree with the names of as many of your great grandparents as you know. Leave gaps for ones you don't yet know about – you may still find out about them. The tree on pages 64 and 65 shows just the *direct line* – if you've got brothers and sisters and want to add them in, draw some extra boxes alongside your own name.

If you want to draw out an even bigger family tree with more side 'branches' (your aunts and uncles, cousins, Great Aunt Sophie, and so on), here are a few tips. You'll find a more detailed tree gets rather wide, because you have to keep people of the same generation side by side so:

1 Use sheets (perhaps A3 or A1) which can be folded up into A4 sections for photocopying (to send to other members of your family).

2 Keep people of the same generation, e.g. you and your cousins, level with each other.

3 Make entries on each person deep rather than broad, to leave more room for others, e.g. five short lines on a person are better than two long lines.

You can put your longer family tree in your Family Album or in a roll in your Family Treasure Chest.

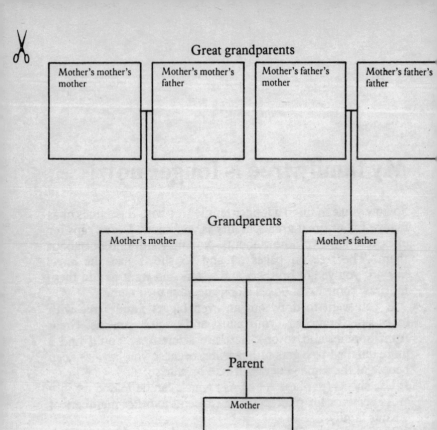

Great grandparents

| Mother's mother's mother | Mother's mother's father | Mother's father's mother | Mother's father's father |

Grandparents

| Mother's mother | Mother's father |

Parent

| Mother |

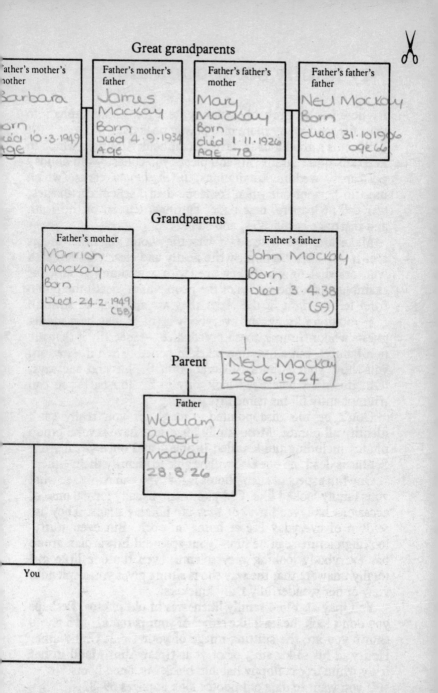

Great grandparents

Father's mother's mother	Father's mother's father	Father's father's mother	Father's father's father
Barbara	James Mackay	Mary Mackay	Neil Mackay
Born	Born	Born	Born
died 10.3.1949	Died 4.9.1934	died 1.11.1926	died 31.10.1906
age	Age	Age 78	age 66

Grandparents

Father's mother	Father's father
Marrion Mackay	John Mackay
Born	Born
Died 24.2.1949 (58)	Died 3.4.38 (59)

Parent

Neil Mackay
28.6.1924

Father

William Robert Mackay
28.8.26

You

My family scrapbook album

By now you've probably stuck quite a few photographs into your file, and many more into plastic pockets.

But it is a good idea to have a Scrapbook Album in which to keep any other family bits and pieces you collect – old holiday postcards, wedding invitations, *in memoriam* cards (which used to be sent out when someone died), school certificates, war call-up papers, newspaper cuttings, letters, birth, death and marriage certificates, and so on.

Make sure you write down what the photos and other things are. If you stick them in, write neatly and clearly underneath who or what or when they are (with a wedding group, for example, write the names of the people underneath the photo from left to right in the order they are standing or sitting).

If you don't know who everybody is (there may be wedding guests whom Granny doesn't recognize – especially if they are non-family), put a question mark in pencil. Then if, later on, you show your Album to Great Aunt Sophie and she says, 'Oh, doesn't Uncle Fred look silly in his top hat!' you can triumphantly fill his name in!

Don't be too disappointed, though, if you really can't identify all photos. Most family historians have several group photos including unidentified people – and once Great Aunt Sophie is dead, no one else will be able to identify them either!

One fun aspect of such photos is that you can really see what your family looked like. Old photos are usually formal ones of occasions like weddings, or they are holiday snaps. They are seldom of everyday life at home or work. But even stuffy-looking pictures can be fun – your splendid Edwardian group has everybody looking very solemn, even the one little girl totally unaware that the way she is sitting gives you a splendid view of her wonderfully frilly knickers!

You may also find family likenesses in old photos. Perhaps you don't look the least like either of your parents, but a photo shows you are the spitting image of your Great Grandfather Henry in his sailor suit, or of your Great Aunt Maud in her frilly white frock, floppy hat and black buttoned boots.

If you want to date old photos look at pages 69–82.

My family treasure chest

What can you do with three-dimensional objects that just won't go into any book or file? – the family bric-à-brac like the smoking cap a great great uncle brought back from the Crimea, christening mugs, napkin rings, spoons, medals, commemorative coins like the Churchill crown, Jubilee and Coronation mugs, old diaries, Birthday Books, samplers (pieces of embroidery worked by young girls, often including name and date), passports, prizes (frequently with a family name inside), badges, old parish magazines, school magazines, ration books, clothing coupons, and so on – the list is endless.

To display these you need either a shelf or a glass cupboard or a 'family box' where you can keep them all together.

If you use a box, you'll have to wrap breakables up carefully in newspaper or tissue paper. And when you look at things, take them out carefully one at a time. Don't churn them all around – or that precious tiny porcelain doll Great Aunt Maud had as a child may get broken.

What would make a good Family Treasure Chest? Well, if you're very lucky, you might have or get given one of those super wooden workboxes, but a strong grocery carton with a four-flap lid would do just as well.

Attach clear labels firmly to all your treasures, and put a list of the contents inside the box lid, together with the names of the people who owned or gave the things to you. A copy of the list along the lines of the one on the next page would be a nice addition to your file.

If you are lucky enough to inherit an old Family Bible, this is a great prize! Look after it especially carefully – it can be a wonderful source of family information, as well as being precious in itself. Family Bibles were often given to young married couples and they entered the births of their children, as well as family marriages and deaths, on a special page.

The more family bits and pieces you collect, the more you will begin to feel your ancestors were real people – just like you!

What's in my family treasure chest

Object	Belonged to	Given to me by	Date
button hook	great grandmother	grandmother (father's mother)	1981
evening purse	grandmother (mother's mother)	grandmother	1982
china doll	great aunt	mother	1983

How to date old pictures

Often you find an old photo or other picture without a date and you'd like to guess roughly when it was taken – especially as an approximate date would help you to give ages to members of your family in it.

Dating things is a big and complex subject, but sometimes the sort of vehicles around (*see pages 78–80*) gives a clue – anything with a motor omnibus in the background must be after the 1890s when motorbuses were developed. Houses usually aren't very much help in themselves. Just because there is a Tudor house in a photograph doesn't mean the people in front of it are Tudor! Some fairly recent house styles are very distinctive, so a picture with the 20s/30s 'Odeon' style of house in it must be after that, but – beware! – lots of house styles are copied at later periods like the many mock-Georgian houses being built today. However, sometimes a street name can give a clue – 'Mafeking Terrace' is bound to be named after 1900 (*see page 89*) – and sometimes there are other clues too – white lines in the road mean the photo was taken after 1912, and Belisha beacons show it was taken after 1934.

However, often the best thing to look at is the clothes the people are wearing. Although fashions change frequently – even every year – there is usually a general overall look to a period that helps you date it roughly. Look at a picture of your parents or grandparents when they were young and see how different their clothes look from yours.

Of course, it's not at all easy to date clothes to an *exact* year. A lot depends on which part of the country the people lived in, how rich or poor they were, and also on their ages. Before rapid transport and television, what was high fashion in London used to take several years to trickle through the rest of the country – and, in the same way, out-of-date fashions tended to linger on in country areas long after people in London were wearing new styles. A good recent example of this was the mini-skirt of the 60s which was still around in the provinces well through the 1970s, until the early 80s London fashions overtook it!

Another problem in dating clothes is that poorer people obviously can't keep up with high fashion, and only gradually alter the style of their clothes as they can afford new ones – and most of our ancestors were very far from being rich! Often, too, older people still dress and do their hair in styles they wore when they were young.

However, despite all that, you can often date a picture to within a decade. Women's clothes usually have the most clues. The next few pages show typical clothes for both adults and children at intervals since the beginning of the nineteenth century. Although they are mostly fashionable clothes, they do give a reasonable picture of the general trends that ordinary people (most of our ancestors!) would be wearing over the period.

The following pages are not marked with the scissors cut out symbol but you might like to keep them all the same.

Clothes

1810s

Straight, high-waisted flimsy dresses for women and girls, with turbans, gypsy straw hats or poke bonnets. Many men wore skin-tight trousers instead of knee breeches, with tail-coats and low top hats. Workmen had jackets, neckerchiefs and felt hats. Boys often had short jackets buttoned onto their trousers.

1830s

A woman's outline was now two triangles meeting at the waist, with huge balloon sleeves, full skirt and vast hat. Many men's waists too were pinched in with corsets under a puffed-out shirt front. Often they wore a frock coat and a tall top hat. All children wore trousers – little boys under a tunic frock; girls as frilly pantalettes, and older boys with a short Eton jacket.

1850s

Women wore enormous full skirts over up to ten petticoats or a wire crinoline cage. They had lace caps indoors and a bonnet out. Many men started wearing more comfortable short jackets for the country. Girls had very low necked frocks with short sleeves and sashes. Boys usually wore belted tunics until they were about nine or ten, and then a matching jacket and long trousers.

1880s

From the late 1860s women's and girls' skirts were pulled to the back over a pad called a bustle. They now wore hats instead of bonnets. Men often wore lounge suits for everyday, with a bowler hat. Boys often had knickerbocker suits, and most girls still wore pinafores over their everyday dresses, and buttoned boots on their feet.

1890s

Fashionable women had 'hourglass' figures, with two-piece costumes, high-necked blouses and leg-of-mutton sleeves. For bicycling and tennis, skirts were often shorter. Girls' dresses were looser now, hanging from a yoke. Sailor suits were very popular for children and continued for many years. Summer hats were often boaters, and men wore knickerbockers in the country.

1900s

The 'S-line' was fashionable for women, with pouter pigeon chests above, and flared skirts below, their tight waists. Huge top-heavy picture hats were loaded with flowers and feathers. Small boys were sometimes crammed into velvet-and-lace Fauntleroy suits. Girls had frilly white dresses, with low-slung sashes and oversize hats.

1910s

Women's skirts were straighter and cleared the ground, with lots of droopy folds, or 'pegtops' (tight at the ankles and wide at the hips). Gradually children were getting into more comfortable shoes and socks. Girls often wore straightish, simple dresses with low belts. Boys dressed more or less like their fathers, except their trousers were short.

1920s

Women's skirts rose after the First World War – even daringly up to the knee. They often cut their hair short (called 'shingling') and wore small, pull-on hats. Men wore Oxford bags and sports jackets for the country. Girls could now wear simple jumpers and skirts, and long socks. Small children often went outdoors in coat and leggings.

1930s

Women's skirts grew longer again, but more slinky, with jaunty hats with veils. Hair was often permanently waved. Men looked like gangsters with long overcoats or rain coats and trilby hats. Boys wore a grey flannel suit and knee socks, with short trousers until they were about thirteen. This fashion lasted for decades. So did the girls' waisted cotton frocks and ankle socks.

1940s

During wartime, cloth was scarce and clothes were rationed, so skirts were short and dresses had draped bodices and square padded boxy masculine-looking shoulders. Hats were small and fussy with veils, though many women wore sensible headscarves. Their hair was done in page-boy bobs, or rolls, or with filmstar curls flopping over one eye. Girls often had pigtails.

1950s

The New Look of 1947 gave women very full, circular skirts
held out with stiff petticoats. The neat, straight suit also came
in. Girls often wore ponytails. Little boys started to wear long
trousers. Many women stopped wearing hats, and everybody
dressed more casually.

1960s

Enter the mini-skirt (more daring than any previous fashions)
worn with high boots or textured stockings to 'bridge the gap'
and lots of long, long hair. Men and boys grew their hair long
too. Jeans could now be worn to work by men, and trousers by
women. Girls wore an unwaisted shift dress.

My fashion forecasts

It's good fun to look at magazines (especially those a year or so old), and try to work out which fashions *you* think will be typical of the 1970s and 1980s. Draw pictures of your ideas, if you can, so that you will be able to look back in years to come and see if your predictions were right! Maybe you could cut some pictures out of the magazines and keep them in your file.

Transport

People today travel a great deal. But your ancestors probably didn't travel farther than the nearest market town. Some people never even left the village in which they were born. Roads were dusty in summer, and a sea of mud in winter. People either walked or, if they could afford it, rode on horseback or stage coach. Gradually, road surfaces improved, and faster vehicles were invented. People's lives changed dramatically as they moved around more.

Inventions or vehicles do help you when dating pictures. You can say that such and such a photograph *must* be later than the 1880s because there's a motor car in it. The next two pages show some of the main steps forward in vehicles since the 1800s – and any photo or object with one of them in *has* to be later than the date it was invented, or became common. If you are not sure what any of the vehicles is like, look it up in an encyclopaedia or general history of transport.

If you want to take dating pictures a stage further and look up the vehicle (say, a motor car) in a specialist history of cars, you might then find out when that particular model was in use, and so be able to date the picture more accurately. For example, Model T Fords were introduced in 1908. But generally, if you reckon the picture must be dated after 1885 when cars were invented, and probably after 1896 when the abolition of the 'Red Flag' act allowed cars to go freely on the roads in Britain, and if you gather any other hints the picture may give you (*see pages 81–82*), you will be able to say fairly confidently, 'This picture was taken around 1905' – or whenever.

If you kept the pages on clothes, you will want to keep the next pages too.

Vehicles since 1800

Single year dates given are usually those of the vehicle's invention or introduction into Britain. Dates like 1860s are usually when the vehicles became fairly common, unless otherwise shown.

First successful steamships
(paddle wheel)
1800s

Hobbyhorse/dandyhorse
(bicycle with no pedals)
1817

Horse cab (London)
1820s

Horse-drawn omnibus
1829

Regular passenger train
services
1830s

Horse-drawn trams
1860s

Velocipede ('boneshaker')
bicycle (front wheel drive)
1860s

First underground railways
1863

Steam trams
1870s

Hansom cab
1834

Macmillan's back-wheel
driven bicycle
1839

Double-decker horsebuses
1840s–1850s

Horse-drawn (steam) fire
engines common
1860s

Penny farthing bicycles
1870s

'Safety' bicycles marketed
1880s

First motor cars
1880s–1890s

First regular motor omnibus
services
1890s–1900s

Motor bikes mass produced
1890s–1900s

Electric trams
1890s–1900s

First real aeroplane
1903

Motor taxis
1900s

Self-propelled (steam and
then motor) fire engines
introduced
1900s

First double-decker motor
buses
1900s

Austin Seven car
1922 – cheap enough for
many thousands to buy

Closed top buses
1920s–1930s

Electric trolley buses
common 1930s (although
around since 1910s)

Closed cars fairly general
1930s

First successful helicopters
1940s

Commercial passenger
jetplanes
1950s

Model T Ford ('Tin Lizzie')
1908 – more cars about
driven by ordinary (i.e. not
rich) people

Last horse buses
1911–14

First practical hovercraft
1959

Mini cars
1960s

Jumbo jets
1970s

Flying boats/ seaplanes
about 1914

Other things that may help to date pictures

Here are a few other items that may help you date old pictures, though they are taken very much at random and you can probably find lots more in books about the period.

Obviously you won't find any actual *photographs* before photography was invented! Photos *could* be reproduced in the 1830s, but weren't popular for many years. By the 1860s however, most homes had a picture gallery of relations on the piano or mantelpiece, and there was a mania for seaside snapshots after pocket cameras were invented in the 1890s. It is supposed to be possible to date studio portraits by the type of *background* used – for example, balustrade, column and curtain are from 1860s; rustic bridge and stile, 1870s; hammock, swing and railway carriage, 1880s; palm trees, cockatoos and bicycles, 1890s, and motor cycles and sidecars, early twentieth century.

As with the vehicles on pages 79–80 specific dates given are usually of the item's invention, and generalized dates show when it became common or popular.

Men's pigtails disappear 1808

Gas street lighting 1810s

'Peelers' (policemen) in top hats 1829

Lawnmowers 1830s (thereafter most lawns will show obvious 'swathes' across them when cut)

Gas lighting common in *town* houses 1840s

Early Christmas cards 1840s

Christmas trees introduced 1840s

'Bloomers' for 'progressive' women about 1849

Croquet very popular 1850s

Policemen wearing helmets 1864

Telephone invented 1870s

Phonograph (gramophone/record player with cylinder) invented 1870s

Red cylindrical pillar boxes general 1876

Deckchairs invented 1880s

First 'school' ties 1880s

Electric lighting available for homes 1880s

Tennis very popular by 1890

Bicycling very popular recreation 1890s

'Red Flag' act abolished 1896, so many more cars around on roads

Holidays at seaside and country (for more than just well-off people) by 1900

Electric light in streets fairly common 1900s (though around since 1870s)

Car number plates 1903

Colour photographs 1900s (direct, i.e. not hand tinted)

Boy Scouts 1907/8

Girl Guides 1910

Telephones in many homes 1911 onwards

White lines in road 1912

Electric lighting more common in homes about 1914

Sunglasses 1920s

Radio sets 1920s

Electric traffic lights 1920s

Neon signs 1930s

'Cats eyes' in road 1930s

Belisha beacons 1934

Television sets in homes after 1936, but not common until 1950s

Fluorescent lights in homes and streets 1940s

Parking meters (in London) 1958

Colour television sets more common 1960s

Do you remember, Granny?

If your granny, grandad or other older relative is willing, get them to look at the buses, cars and planes etc. on pages 79 and 80 or the list of miscellaneous happenings on pages 81 and 82. Ask them what they remember. Does Granny remember when her house changed from gas to electric lighting, or her first ride in a motor bus, or white lines being painted in the road, or the first jet plane? Ask her to write it down here.

Event or Thing Remembered	Date	Name	Relationship to me

Time charts

The following pages cover some of the most important or noteworthy events over the years since 1800 – events that either took place in the British Isles, or affected the people there, or events in other countries that were news there. You could ask your relatives to look through the charts (starting at the most recent dates and working backwards). Then get them to write down in the boxes on pages 86–98 their names and ages opposite the first great event they *really* remember. For example, Battle of Alamein – George Stubbs (my grandfather), age 10.

For long-ago events you yourself might like to fill in the name of an ancestor who is now dead, but who might have seen or been alive when the event took place.

Do this for several relatives and you'll find it great fun and very interesting. You won't be able to fill in all the boxes, of course – and also, if several relatives have seen the *same* event, they won't all be able to put their names in the boxes. They could perhaps use the chart opposite.

If you want to find out more about the *details* of an event, look it up in a good encyclopaedia, or history book of the period.

Also, you can ask your family, especially elderly relatives, what other events or happenings they remember, and fill those in on the chart opposite too. Ask them as well to look at pages 91 and 92, 95 and 96, about the First and Second World Wars.

Pages 99 and 100 are especially for *you* to fill in great events as they happened that you think you will want to tell your children and grandchildren about!

Event or thing remembered	Date	Name	Relationship to me

1800–1850

Date	Event	Could have been seen or remembered by
1800/1	Act of Union made Ireland part of United Kingdom	*Name* *Age*
1805	Battle of Trafalgar, death of Nelson	*Name* *Age*
1812	Napoleon's retreat from Moscow; War with USA	*Name* *Age*
1815	Battle of Waterloo	*Name* *Age*
1820	George III died, Prince Regent, became George IV	*Name* *Age*
1825	First passenger railway – Stockton to Darlington	*Name* *Age*
1830	George IV died, William IV king	*Name* *Age*
1832	Great Reform Bill passed	*Name* *Age*
1833	Abolition of Slavery throughout British Empire	*Name* *Age*
1834	Tolpuddle Martyrs transported	*Name* *Age*
1837	Death of William IV, Victoria queen	*Name* *Age*
1840	Introduction of Penny Post	*Name* *Age*

1850–1900

Date	Event	Could have been seen or remembered by
1851	Great Exhibition at Crystal Palace.	Name Age
1851	Gold discovered in Australia.	Name Age
1854	Crimean War started	Name Age
1854	Charge of Light Brigade (Battle of Balaclava)	Name Age
1855	Florence Nightingale set up hospital at Scutari.	Name Age
1857	Indian Mutiny.	Name Age
1861	Prince Albert died.	Name Age
1861	American Civil War started.	Name Age
1865	President Abraham Lincoln assassinated.	Name Age
1868	Last public execution in Britain.	Name Age
1869	Suez Canal opened.	Name Age
1870	Board schools set up to spread elementary education.	Name Age
1870	Franco-Prussian War.	Name Age

Date	Event	Could have been seen or remembered by
1871	First Bank Holidays.	Name Age
1871	Stanley found Dr Livingstone at Ujiji in Africa.	Name Age
1872	Secret Ballot for elections.	Name Age
1875	Boy chimney sweeps banned.	Name Age
1879	Zulu War, Rorke's Drift.	Name Age
1885	General Gordon killed at Khartoum.	Name Age
1887	Queen Victoria's Golden Jubilee.	Name Age
1896	First public (silent) film show in London.	Name Age
1896	Jameson Raid failed.	Name Age
1897	Queen Victoria's Diamond Jubilee.	Name Age
1899	Boer War started.	Name Age

1900–1930

Date	Event	Seen or remembered by
1900	Ladysmith and Mafeking relieved	*Name* *Age*
1901	Queen Victoria died, Edward VII king	*Name* *Age*
1902	End of Boer War	*Name* *Age*
1903	Wright Brothers flew first real aeroplane	*Name* *Age*
1909	Blériot flew English Channel	*Name* *Age*
1910	Edward VII died, George V king	*Name* *Age*
1912	Sinking of the *Titanic*	*Name* *Age*
1913	Suffragette killed by throwing herself under king's horse at Derby Race	*Name* *Age*
1914	First World War started – see also next pages	*Name* *Age*
1914	Battles of Mons and the Marne, and First Battle of Ypres started	*Name* *Age*
1915	Second Battle of Ypres and of Loos	*Name* *Age*
1915	Gallipoli (Dardanelles) Campaign	*Name* *Age*

1915	Sinking of *Lusitania*	Name Age
1916	Battles of Verdun and the Somme; Battle of Jutland	Name Age
1916	Easter Rising in Dublin	Name Age
1917	Battle of Passchendaele (third Battle of Ypres)	Name Age
1917	Tank battle at Cambrai	Name Age
1917	Russian Revolution	Name Age
1917	America entered war	Name Age
1918	End of First World War	Name Age
1919	Alcock and Brown flew Atlantic non-stop	Name Age
1922	Civil War in Ireland after Irish Free State set up in 1921	Name Age
1922	First daily radio broadcast	Name Age
1926	General Strike	Name Age
1927	First 'talking' films	Name Age
1929	Wall Street Crash and start of Great Depression	Name Age

The First World War (1914-18)

Some of your very elderly relatives may actually remember the First World War. A very old grandfather, great grandfather or great uncle may even have fought in one of the battles listed on pages 89 and 90, and a granny or great aunt may have been a nurse or VAD (member of the Voluntary Aid Department), or done other war work.

Even if they were only small children at the time, they may remember bits of the war as it affected them and their parents. Ask them to tell you about it so you can write down on page 92 what they remember. Stick in any souvenirs they may give you – or put them carefully in your Treasure Chest. (If nobody remembers it, perhaps you could stick in other general pictures of the War.)

To get your relatives talking, ask if they remember any of these:

Declaration of war on 4 August, 1914
Knitting for the troops
Father, brother, fiancé, husband or friend going off to fight
Father etc coming home on leave
Someone they knew being killed at the Front
Christmas truce of 1914
Zeppelins being shot down
British Summer Time (daylight saving) introduced, 1916
Bombing (though there was not nearly as much in the First World War as in the Second War)
Food shortages
Armistice Day, 11 November, 1918
Father, brother, etc being demobbed
Unveiling of Cenotaph by King George V and burial of Unknown Soldier in Westminster Abbey, 1920.

Things I remember about the First World War by

....

Date	Event	Seen or remembered by
1936	Death of King George V, abdication of Edward VIII	*Name* *Age*
1936	Spanish Civil War started	*Name* *Age*
1937	Coronation of George VI	*Name* *Age*
1938	Munich Agreement	*Name* *Age*
1939	Second World War began – see also next pages	*Name* *Age*
1940	Dunkirk	*Name* *Age*
1940	Battle of Britain	*Name* *Age*
1940–41	Blitz	*Name* *Age*
1941	Japanese bombed Pearl Harbour, America entered war	*Name* *Age*
1942	Fall of Singapore	*Name* *Age*
1942	Battle of Alamein	*Name* *Age*
1943	German army surrendered at Stalingrad	*Name* *Age*
1943	Allies invaded Sicily and Italian mainland	*Name* *Age*

1944	'D Day' (6 June) landings in Normandy, Battle of Arnhem	*Name* *Age*
1944	V1 ('doodlebugs'/ flying bombs) fell on Britain	*Name* *Age*
1944	V2 rockets	*Name* *Age*
1945	V-E Day – 'Victory over Europe' to celebrate German surrender on 8 May	*Name* *Age*
1945	Atomic bombs dropped on Hiroshima and Nagasaki	*Name* *Age*
1945	V-J Day – 'Victory over Japan' to celebrate Japanese surrender and therefore end of war on 14 August	*Name* *Age*
1947	Partition of India and Pakistan	*Name* *Age*
1947	'New Look' clothes for women	*Name* *Age*
1947	Princess Elizabeth's wedding to Lieutenant Philip Mountbatten	*Name* *Age*
1948	State of Israel set up	*Name* *Age*
1948	Prince Charles born	*Name* *Age*

The Second World War (1939-45)

Many of your older relatives will probably remember quite a lot about this War – ask them to tell you what they remember and write it down on page 96. Stick in any souvenirs they can give you. Here are a few 'Do you remembers?' to get them started:

Declaration of war (3 September, 1939)
Churchill's broadcasts
The King's Christmas broadcasts
Children being evacuated
Gas masks
Bombing
House bombed – or windows broken etc
Fire watching
Blackout
Sirens (Alert and All-clear)
Barbed wire on seaside beaches
Shelters (Anderson, Morrison etc)
Rationing (dried egg, National Loaf etc)
Home Guard (Dad's Army)
Anyone they knew going to fight or be a nurse at the Front
Double Summer Time
Black Market
End of the war
Victory celebrations (V-E and V-J days)
First banana
First icecream after war
Father's coming home after war etc.

Things I remember about the Second World War by

....

1950–1980

As well as asking your relatives to fill in these, you can fill in the later ones you yourself remember. See also pages 99 and 100.

Date	Event	Seen or remembered by
1950	Korean War	Name Age
1952	Death of King George VI	Name Age
1953	Food rationing finally ends	Name Age
1953	Conquest of Mt Everest, Coronation of Elizabeth II	Name Age
1956	Suez Crisis	Name Age
1956	Hungarian Uprising	Name Age
1957	First space flight (Sputnik)	Name Age
1961	First man in space (Yuri Gagarin)	Name Age
1963	President Kennedy assassinated	Name Age
1965	American troops fighting in Vietnam War	Name Age
1965	Winston Churchill's funeral	Name Age
1965	UDI in Rhodesia (now Zimbabwe)	Name Age

1966	England won World Cup	Name Age
1968	Russians invaded Czechoslovakia	Name Age
1968	Martin Luther King and Robert Kennedy assassinated	Name Age
1969	Americans landed on moon	Name Age
1969	Troubles start again in Northern Ireland	Name Age
1971	Decimal coinage in Britain	Name Age
1973	Britain entered Common Market	Name Age
1974	President Nixon resigned after Watergate scandal	Name Age
1976	Concorde in service	Name Age
1977	Queen Elizabeth's Silver Jubilee	Name Age
1978	World's first test tube baby	Name Age
1979	Britain has first woman Prime Minister (Margaret Thatcher)	Name Age

I remember that!

Use the next two pages to put down special events you think you will remember in the future and want to tell your children and grandchildren about. Add any newspaper cuttings or other souvenirs you get. Keep it up over a few years – you could even start up a special *Events Scrapbook* for it – you'll find it great fun to keep and look back at. Your list might begin something like this:

1981 Poland – Solidarity movement forced underground
1981 Royal Wedding between Prince Charles and Lady Diana Spencer.
1981 Columbia (first Space Shuttle) launched
1982 Falklands Conflict April–June
1982 Visit of Pope John Paul II to Great Britain.
1982 Birth of Prince William of Wales, heir apparent to the throne, 21 June.

I remember that! (continued)

Other kinds of family trees

Let's leave the great events now and get back to the family trail again – you now know how to draw the kind of family tree which can show clearly several branches of your family at once. There are some other kinds of family tree, too, which show only your direct ancestors. You can fill these in, if you like.

This one is called a birth brief. It starts with you on the left and goes sideways across the page like this:

YOU	Mother	Grandmother
		Grandfather
	Father	Grandmother
		Grandfather

Here is another way of doing a family tree of your direct ancestors – in a circle. Start with yourself in the middle and work outwards, a ring for each generation.

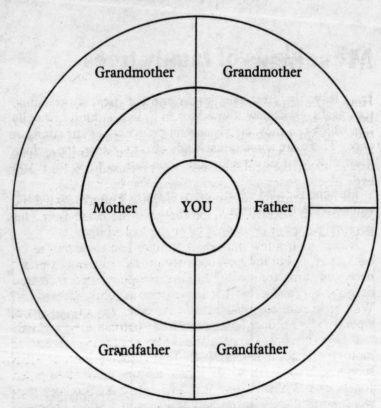

With all trees you can, of course, add brief details of birth, marriage and death dates. Abbreviations like *b*. 1910, *m*. 1940, *d*. 1975 are fine.

With the circle kind, it's fun also to put a pair of ancestors, say one pair of great grandparents, in the middle of another circle and work outwards, filling in their descendants.

My surname

However much or little you can find out about nearer members of your family, you have at least one essential clue to your more distant ancestors – your surname. Surnames have been around a very long time, so you are unlikely to find out any details about the actual person who first used it – even very experienced genealogists seldom get as far back as that.

But your surname can often give you a hint as to what job your distant ancestor did, or the place he came from, his parents' names or even what he or she looked like.

How? Well, a few important families had surnames as far back as 1066, but for most ordinary people, surnames weren't necessary until around 1250. Then the population increased dramatically, and a few first names such as John, Richard and William became so popular that some other way of identifying a person was needed. So an extra name (surname) was added.

Many surnames were given after a person's father or mother – names like Johnson or Johns (John's son), or Allisson (Alice's son). (In Wales John's son was more often called Jones, and William's son Williams, while in Scotland they were more often Johnson and Williamson.) Many abbreviations were used as well, so William's son could also be called Will, Wilson, Wilkins, Wilkes and Willett. Sometimes surnames were based on rhymes. Hodge and Dodge were a popular rhyming version of Roger, so as well as Rogerson, Rogers, and Rudge, people called Hodge, Hodgson, Dodd, Dodds and Dodgson all have ancestors called Roger.

Other surnames were given according to a person's job – if the person was a baker, he might be called John the Baker, or John Baker, and if he was a fisherman, Richard Fisher. But beware, Lord, Bishop and Pope as surnames don't mean your ancestor came from church or court! Either he played one of those parts in a play or pageant, or he was so haughty or pious that he was given the name as a joke!

Some surnames were from places – if your ancestor lived in a particular part of the village (near the church, the village green, the brook, the river, the hill or field), his name might be John Church, Richard Green and so on. Or if he had come to the village from another place (Salisbury, say) or perhaps gone as an apprentice boy to London, he might be called John of Salisbury, or John Salisbury. Look up a 'place-name' surname in a gazetteer; if there are lots of different places called the same, you can't really tell where your ancestor came from, but if you are lucky and there's just one entry, you're in business! Though – beware! often the spelling of place names has changed over the years – for example, Bristol used to be spelled 'Bristow'.

Names come from personal characteristics too – if your ancestor was very short or a 'know-all', he might have been called John Short (or John Little), or Richard Wise. However, people liked a joke, so he might have also been called 'Short' because he was very *tall*, just as today some short people are called 'Lofty'.

At first surnames weren't passed down from father to son. If Richard Johnson had a son William, he would have been called William Richardson, (and not William Johnson) but gradually surnames did become fixed and were passed on through the male line of families (women usually took their husband's name when they married).

So if your name is Miller, you can be fairly certain that long ago one of your ancestors ground corn. If it's Smith he was either the village blacksmith or another of the many different types of craftsmen. Though the meanings of some 'occupational' surnames have disappeared along with the actual job – for example, a fletcher was an arrowmaker. It's good fun to look up the meaning of your surname in a *Dictionary of Surnames* (in your local library) and try to find out what it means. Write it down in the space at the bottom of page 106. Don't be depressed, though, if your surname is unusual (or foreign) and so not in the *Dictionary*. You can always *guess* what it might mean. In fact, an unusual surname is a great 'plus' if you want to continue with research into your family as you grow older. If you write down all references to that name in public records, you can be fairly sure that many of them will be your relations – whereas people called Smith have a much harder task!

If your surname is not too common, try looking it up in the telephone directories for the whole country (in the reference section of the local library or in a main post office). Write down how many times your surname occurs in each directory, e.g. Manchester Central 10 times; Brighton 18 times, and so on.

Directory	District	No. of times my surname occurs

Super Surname Quiz

Here are 20 fairly common surnames. Write down what you think each might mean. Then turn to page 123 to see if you were right.

Surname	*What it might mean*
Appleyard	
Barber	
Cruickshanks	
Dale	
Davies	
Dixon, Dickson	
Fox	
Greenwood	
King	
Lester (Beware! The spelling may have changed)	
Jackson	
Peterson	
Plummer	
Redhead	
Stranger	
Taylor	
Townsend	
Underhill	
Vickers (watch the spelling again!)	
Wiseman	

My surname means/or I think it might mean ....

Fashions in names

Christian names can help too. They tend to come in fashions, and can help date ages of people who have them. 'Maud' is fairly likely to have been born at the turn of the century – you won't find many little girls christened Maud today!

Today people usually like to give their children at least one name that is different from their own, but from 1600 to 1900 it was normal to call the first son after his father or one of his grandfathers. Second and third sons were also given family names, and only then did parents choose something a bit different. Often these 'different' names were the ones that were fashionable at the time, and these can help in dating ages, and also in tracing members of the same family.

The top few favourite names tended to stay constant – from 1600 to 1649 the 'top-three' girls names were Elizabeth, Mary and Anne, and they are still very popular today. In fact, John has been the most popular boy's name for over 700 years! So finding a family with your surname and Johns in several generations isn't going to help you much, but if alongside the Johns you find several Nathaniels and Ambroses, these more unusual names point to the fact that they may all be members of the same branch of the family – called after each other.

However, when trying to link names like this you do have to be careful. In earlier times so many babies and small children died that often parents gave the same name to several children – in the sad hope that one might survive! A family tomb may even have a whole clutch of little brothers called Nathaniel. In fact, if a child was sickly, the next one might even be given the same name while the first one was still alive! Very occasionally the first one surprised everyone by surviving – so you may even find a reference to 'my sons Nathaniel Stubbs the elder, and Nathaniel Stubbs the younger'!

How did names change over the centuries? The Anglo-Saxons had many names now long forgotten, but the Normans brought in sturdy names like William, Richard, Robert and Henry – and the biblical John. Throughout the Middle Ages there were lots of Marys, Elizabeths, Janes and Annes, Catherines, Margarets and Sarahs.

The seventeenth century Puritans had worthy, moral names like Faith, Hope, Charity, Prudence – and ones we don't have any more like Repentance, Obedience and even Thankful!

In the eighteenth century parents often added a second Christian name (sometimes the mother's maiden name or the surname of someone who might leave little Frederick something in his will!) Later on in the century and in the early nineteenth, classical names became fashionable. Mary became Maria: her sisters might be Julia, Sophia, Augusta, and her brothers Horace, Septimus or Octavius.

In later Victorian and Edwardian times there was a revival of Old English names – Edith, Hilda, Edwin, Wilfred, Alfred and Maud along with names like Bertha, Ada, Pearl, Stanley, Herbert, Sidney and Humphrey – all giving invaluable clues in guessing ages.

'What's his Name?' Quiz

In the boxes below are some fairly popular names in recent times, as well as ones that have been popular for hundreds of years. Look in the *Births* column of a newspaper every day for a month and tick off each time you see one of these names. Write down any other names that interest you – your own if it isn't one of these, for example, and tick this off too. Do the same in the other columns for members of your family past and present, or members of your class at school. What do you find? Which names were most popular?

Boys' Names	Newspaper	In my family	In my class
John			
William			
Richard			
Robert			
Henry			
James			
Edward			
Charles			
David			
Daniel			
Dominic			
Luke			
Marcus			
Jason			
Lee			

Girls' Names	Newspaper	In my family	In my class
Elizabeth			
Mary			
Jane			
Anne			
Lucy			
Catherine/Katharine			
Sarah			
Margaret			
Caroline			
Emma			
Victoria			
Samantha			
Melanie			
Tracey			
Alice			

*Other names that
interest me*

Delving further back (official records)

Back on the family trail again! Your great grandparents' parents are your great great grandparents; *their* parents – your great great great grandparents – and so on! If you want now – or later on – to dig deeper into your family history and find out about these people (or if you want to check on some of the oral information you've already got), you'll most likely have to check in the official public records.

Now you get into a really complicated detective search – and this book can only give you a taste of how to set about it. There are lots of more detailed books to help you – some of them are on page 126.

Basically what you need to know is this: From 1837 all births, deaths and marriages for people actually born in England and Wales are recorded centrally at St Catherine's House, Kingsway, London. (You will often hear people calling this place 'Somerset House' – where the records used to be kept, but they are actually now in St Catherine's). Scotland, Northern Ireland and Eire have their own separate Record Offices.

You can search in these central offices; but if you know that after 1837 your family settled in one area for some time it's possibly better to go to the local District Registry Office, – especially if you live a long way from London, Edinburgh, Belfast or Dublin.

If you do go to St Catherine's, there are big Indexes for all the Births, Marriages and Deaths (separate ones for each) and you can use these for free. There are four volumes for each year, one for each quarter. The entries for each birth, death or marriage are in alphabetical order of surnames, with a reference number by them (e.g. I.206 SH). These index volumes are jolly heavy! So, before you break your arms lifting down volume after volume, it's a good idea to get an 'oral' lead from Great Aunt Sophie on where to start looking – 'I think your great great grandfather was born about the time of the Battle of Balaclava, dear.' So start looking about or even just before 1854.

Once you get the reference number, you can pay to have a copy of the birth, marriage or death certificate you need. It'll cost several pounds, and it's much dearer by post. (So if you can't get there yourself, try to get a friend to go there for you!)

Before 1837, births, marriages and deaths were usually recorded in registers in the person's parish church (called parish registers), or if he or she was non-conformist, Catholic, Quaker or Jewish, etc. perhaps in these sectarian registers, often kept nowadays in the Public Record Office, or at the central offices/library of the relevant sect (*see below and also page 124*).

For ordinary Church of England parish registers you need to know the district and, if possible, the parish church where your ancestor lived. If you *don't* know what parish he was born in, but do know where he was living in a census year (a date ending in the figure 1), you could try the Census records at the Public Record Office (*see page 114*). When you do find out the parish, try the County Record Office for the area. Many of them have copies of parish registers, and for a fee they will search for you, or you could go with a grown up and look yourself for free.

If the registers *aren't* in the County Record Office, write to the clergyman in charge of the church today, and see if he will help – you should offer to pay him for his trouble. If you can go to the church with a grown up, you may even be allowed to look at the registers yourself. Be *very* careful with them – they're very precious. Remember too, that old handwriting can be very difficult to read, and spellings may vary a lot as well!

If you *know* your ancestors were Jewish or Roman Catholic or of a non-Church of England denomination, write to the Head Office of the relevant group and see where their records are kept.

If your ancestors came from or went overseas, you could try the Mormon records centralised in Salt Lake City, USA.

There are fortunately local branches in this country (*see page 124*) but do get a 'lead' as to where to start first, and be patient – you'll have to wait several months for the information you want. The Mormons also have a Computer File Index (also called the International Genealogical Index) which has millions of ordinary (i.e. non-Mormon) births or baptisms for this country entered on microfilm. In fact, this is probably nowadays the *first* place to look – *before* parish registers in the County Record Office.

Page 124 gives some useful addresses but, as these might change, do check them as well as times of opening and fees payable before making a special journey.

Counting everybody (the national census)

Every ten years since 1801 (except during World War II) a national Census (counting of the population) has been held. Every householder fills in a form about all the people in his house on Census Night – their ages, jobs, place of birth, etc. and what relationship they are to each other.

Census returns are very useful to the family historian, because the fact that the person's place of birth is given shows him where to go to search parish registers; the job description often shows *what* his ancestor was doing, and it often reveals details about the family that he couldn't otherwise have known – the names of children in the family who may have died in infancy.

Big libraries often have copies of the Census returns. They have to be over a hundred years old to be published – look at those for 1851, 1861, 1871 and 1881. (Earlier ones published are not much use to family historians, although the 1841 census has *some* information.) If you are lucky enough to know where your ancestor was living in, say, 1871, perhaps from a copy of his son's birth certificate around that time, you could try looking him up.

If the returns aren't in a convenient Library, the County Records Office for that area may have them – or you can see those for England and Wales in the national collection at the Public Record Office in London. However, these are on microfilm and the handwriting can be a bit difficult to decipher. (Also, people under ten aren't allowed in!)

Scottish census records are kept at New Register House, Edinburgh, but Irish ones before 1901 were destroyed in 1922.

My birth certificate

Your birth certificate is the piece of paper which proves to the world that you exist – as if you had any real doubt!

Ask at home if they have your birth certificate. You probably won't be able to stick the original in your file, but a careful photocopy will do just as well. You could even colour it pink to look like the real thing.

You could stick one edge down on page 116 like this:

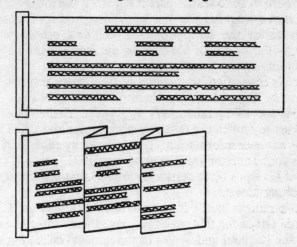

and then fold the rest if it doesn't fit your file; or you could put it into a plastic pocket in your file.

If you can't see a copy at home and your parents agree, go along with them to the Registry Office for Births and Deaths in the area where you were born – or write to the Registrar there for a copy. Look in the telephone directory for the address.

Get a grown-up to help you fill in the form. It'll cost you a few pounds, but it's fun to have and keep.

My birth certificate

Newspaper cuttings

Often local libraries have splendid collections of local newspapers – sometimes even going back to the 1700s. These can tell you a lot about the life and times in which your ancestors lived – local 'gossipy' events, like elopements, factory disasters, burglaries, and so on.

If your family happened to live in a particular place for a long time, you may be able to find references to them in these local papers, especially in the 'Births, Deaths and Marriages' columns or, if they were important enough, in the 'Obituaries'. However this will mean a lot of searching through oceans of small print, so you might prefer to leave it until you feel strong enough to tackle it!

While on the subject of newspapers though, you may find older members of your family have over the years collected cuttings from newspapers on great events, or even articles with their name in it. Perhaps there was a big presentation when your grandfather retired as Group Scoutmaster and it was written up in the local paper. He's very proud of the cutting, and will probably be delighted to let you photocopy it and put it in your file.

If you can't seem to find any of this sort of article, why not start a 'cuttings' page of great events for *your* children to look at. (You've probably still got some cuttings of the Royal Wedding or the Royal Baby or the Falklands Conflict).

My family's autographs

The next few pages are to show you how to start a family autograph collection.

Start off with the people nearest to you – your parents, brothers and sisters, and so on.

Then try ranging farther afield. You could even write a nice letter to distant relatives, explain about this book, and ask them to write their autograph on a small piece of paper so you can stick it in your file.

After each autograph, print clearly the person's name and what relation they are to you.

My autograph

My own notes

These pages have been left blank so you can use them as you like – for extra notes perhaps.

If you make extra notes here – of things you have not room for earlier, or things you want to check on at some later time, it's best to write them in pencil while they are still doubtful. Then you can fill them in later in ink – and make this book a beautiful record of your family and its history.

HAVE FUN!

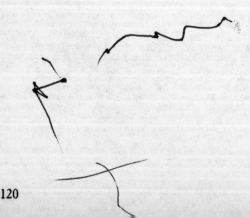

My own notes

My own notes

Answers to quiz

(Super Surname quiz, page 106)

Appleyard – someone who worked or lived in an orchard.

Barber – a trade-name. Barbers not only cut hair – they were also surgeons!

Cruickshanks – a nickname; probably he had crooked legs or knock knees.

Dale – someone who lived in the dale (valley).

Davies – son of David (Davy's son).

Dixon, Dickson – Richard (Dick's) son.

Fox – like the animal – either with reddish colouring, or crafty.

Greenwood – living near the forest.

King – No, not of royal descent – sorry! Either a nickname for someone with royal bearing or rather stuck-up, or someone who played the part of the King in a play or pageant.

Lester – probably someone who came from Leicester.

Jackson – son of John (Jack is short for John).

Peterson – Peter's son.

Plummer – either a real plumber, or someone who dealt in feathers (plumes), or someone connected with plum trees by a mere (pool).

Redhead – nickname for carrot-top.

Stranger – a newcomer to the village.

Taylor – a tailor by trade.

Townsend – someone who came from the end of the town or village.

Underhill – person who lived at the foot of the hill.

Vickers – unlikely to be the vicar's son – clergy not supposed to be married at time surnames were growing up; more likely the vicar's servant.

Wiseman – either he really was wise – or it's an unkind joke – he was the village idiot.

Addresses

As these and opening times may change from time to time, you should check them and any fees payable *before* setting off on a visit. Enclose a stamped addressed envelope.

General Register Office (Office of Populations, Censuses and Surveys), St Catherine's House, 10 Kingsway, London WC2B 6JP (Births, marriages and deaths in England and Wales after 1837)

General Register Office or The Scottish Records Office, New Register House, Edinburgh EH1 3YT (Scottish records)

General Register Office, Oxford House, 49–55 Chichester Street, Belfast BT1 4HI (Northern Ireland records)

General Register Office, Customs House, Dublin 1 (Eire records)

Public Record Office, Census section, Land Registry Building, Portugal Street, London WC2

The Society of Genealogists, 37 Harrington Gardens, London SW7

Federation of Family History Societies, The Drovers, Cambridge, Gloucestershire, GL2 7AN

County Record Offices (for some pre-1837 records and copies of many parish registers) – look in the telephone directory under the name of the county and write to the Archivist in Charge

Parish Churches (for pre-1837 records) – look up the name of the clergyman in charge under the town or village in *Crockford's Clerical Directory* (in the reference section of the public library)

District Register Office (for certificates after 1837 if you are *sure* of the area, and of the date within 5 years) – see in local telephone directory under *Registration of Births, Deaths and Marriages*. Write to the Superintendent Registrar.

The Baptist Historical Society, Baptist Union Library, 4 Southampton Row, London WC1B 4AB

The Catholic Record Society, Archbishops' House, London SW1

Congregational Library, Memorial Hall, Farringdon Street, London EC4

The Jewish Historical Society, 33 Seymour Place, London W1H 5AP and/or The Jewish Museum, Woburn House, Upper Woburn Place, London WC1

The Library of the Society of Friends, Friends House, Euston Road, London NW1 (Quaker records)

The Methodist Archivist Research Centre, 25 City Road, London EC1 and/or Methodist Archives, Division of Property, Central Buildings, Oldham Street, Manchester M1 1SQ

The United Reformed Church Historical Society, 86 Tavistock Place, London WC1

Dr Williams Library, 14 Gordon Square, London WC1H 0AG (Non-conformists generally)

The Genealogical Society, Salt Lake City, Utah, USA (worldwide records – not especially Mormon) but better to try your local Mormon Branch Library first which also will have copies of the International Genealogical Index for the whole of Britain. Write to 64–68 Exhibition Road, London SW7 for the address of your nearest Mormon branch library. International Genealogical Index also at Society of Genealogists (and parts of it on relevant local areas at some libraries and county record offices)

Books to read

If you want to take your search for your family ancestors further at a later date, here are some more detailed books you might read. Ask in your local library to see what books (usually under the numbers 929 on the shelf) they have – it's a popular subject so you may have to order.

Your Family Tree Discovering Series, David Iredale (Shire Publications)

Your Family History C. M. Matthews (Lutterworth Press)

Discovering your Family History Don Steel (BBC Publications)

Beginning your Family History George Pelling (Federation of Family History Societies, 96 Beaumont Street, Milehouse, Plymouth, Devon PL2 3AQ – a useful little booklet)

The Family History Book Stella Colwell (Phaidon Press)

Debrett's Family Historian Noel Currer-Briggs and Royston Gambier (Debrett)

Genealogy for Beginners A. J. Willis (Phillimore & Co)

Tracing your Ancestors Meda Mander (David & Charles)

Index

1900   1936